Archer, Journey to Stonehenge

Jane Brayne

I am a stranger here. This is not my home.

In my own land mountains reached up to the Sun God in the sky.

Eagles circled, eyeing their prey.

Wolves and bears prowled, always hungry.

My people hunt with the bow. Every day I practised my aim.

I learned to make arrowheads and knives from flint

Ouch - I've cut my leg!

Not again - you're rubbish !!

and to speak the languages of other tribes - my people like to go travelling.

That word means STUPID - like her !

No. It means UGLY - like you!

Stop fighting or target practice is banned !

My father was our chieftain.

When I grow up will I be wise and brave enough to lead the tribe?

Things were changing for my sister too.

Soon after that a flint-trading chieftain brought his son to see her.

They came all the way from the Long West River.

The marriage was arranged for the autumn. She had no time for target practice anymore.

The shapes and colours on our clothes tell stories.

chieftain's daughter

from the mountains

Zigzags also speak of good times and bad, of births and deaths; the pattern of a life.

My sister learned to make beakers.

Roll out the clay.

Make a coil for the base.

Build up the sides and smooth out the coils.

Press a string into the clay to decorate the pot.

The women showed her how to set a fire around her pots.

In the fire the soft clay is transformed. It becomes hard, like stone, so that it can last forever...

Sun God — we dedicate our beakers to you !!!

This is women's magic.

You will look so beautiful on your wedding day...

But it's such a long way to the flint mines.

Preparations were going well until...

Cattle thieves !!!

NEXT DAY
You will have to go to the wedding in my place. The raiders might strike again.

Making a long journey will earn you the respect of the tribe. If you're going to become chieftain after me you must prove yourself ready.

Your mother has made you a fine deer-skin cloak and this tunic decorated in the colours of our ancestors.

This stone, shaped and polished in your honour, will brace your wrist-guard and show every-one that you are a chieftain's son.

I will fasten your cloak with my own antler pin, handed down by my father and his father before him.

Maybe I really will be chieftain one day...

Don't you look pretty all dressed up?!

Stop it — you'll tear your new clothes! When will you two act like grown ups?

With aunts and uncles and cousins we set off for my sister's new home. Over the high mountains...

along the lake,

down the Great South River,

overland to the Great West River.

Do you think the people down there are friendly?

Let's find out!

We've brought you gifts — can we stay here tonight?

You are welcome! come and eat at our fireside.

That night we told travellers' tales...

Uncle — tell us the one about your journey to the ocean!

Far away in the West is a place where rocks jut out into the Sea. It is called the Stoneland. Long ago, when we were young, my brothers and I journeyed there to see the distant horizon where the Sun God falls asleep each night beyond the waves.

The sea is turning into molten copper!

It is the blood of the Sun God!!!

My sister had carried one small beaker in her pack, wrapped in soft fox fur.

She meant it as a gift for her husband but now it must go with our uncle to his grave.

We filled the pot with cow's milk to sustain him on his journey.

In the lands which lie beyond this life great beasts roam in the dark forests. One day we will track them together, the wolf, the bear, the boar, the mighty aurochs, whose horns grow longer than a man's arm, the stag, his antlers spread wide, and the shy spotted lynx.
Until then, good hunting Uncle!

NEXT DAY PEOPLE BEGAN TO ARRIVE FOR THE WEDDING.

Welcome friends!

We've come from the Stoneland in the West.

Here's to the lovely couple!

May the Sun God give them lots of children!

I'm going to miss her...

Is there any more ale?

WE FEASTED UNTIL DAWN

Stonelanders - tell us, do you live by the sea?

Each night do you watch the Sun God sink to sleep beneath the waves?

Yes we do. Our home land is a sacred place.

Why not come back with us? Join us for the autumn celebrations at our great Stone temples.

I wish we could but our tribe is troubled by cattle thieves.

And my father was killed on the way here. We must go home.

Boys - you should accept. It's not far and there will always be cattle raids...

Let's go with them - they're too young to travel alone.

Not me. I'll have to take Dad's place at home. But I want you all to go. Your journey will honour his memory.

NEXT DAY

No more fights big brother...

I'll see you again soon - we'll stop off on our way home.

Come on - we need to follow the Stonelanders!

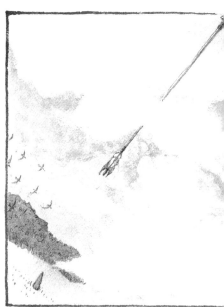

NEXT DAY

Hang on — before you leave...

We come from a land across the sea. We're setting off home tomorrow. You are welcome to travel with us. Our boats are sturdy and the boatmen have made the journey many times.

Come and see our great stone temple. It's the most powerful place in all the world!

We are guardians of the temple. They call us the Observers, those who watch the skies.

At Midwinter, on the longest night of the year, the Sun God travels to our temple to die!

He sinks down deep into the Underworld. Only the Observers have the knowledge and the strength to bring him back into the sky!

Let's go!!!

How do we know we can trust them?

Can we stay for Midwinter?

Your invitation is generous, but we need time to think about it...

If I visit this sacred place to see the Sun God die the people of our tribe will respect me deeply. They will want me for their chieftain.

LATER

I am your chieftain's son. My father made me leader of this party — I say we go!

Me too!

And me!

We can't stop you, but take these copper beads and the ingots too — they're our last ones — in case you have to bargain your way out of trouble.

NEXT DAY

May the Sun God protect you all!

Day after long day we paddled around the coastline, sleeping each night on the shore.

All we had to eat was salty dried fish – the Stonelanders gave us that – seaweed and sea snails, prised off the rocks.

ABOVE THE RIVER

We're always glad to welcome travellers. Have you brought us any copper?

Yes, but they didn't tell us you were smiths.

Wow!

We would like to stay until mid-winter if that's alright...

We'll work hard to earn our keep.

Rain again... no wonder the Sun God wants to die when he comes here...

NEXT DAY

Copper of course! Our magic is new to them. Only we can call the Sun God into our fire!

What do all those people want?

Do you let them watch you at work?

Not too closely - we must keep our secrets. But they pay us well - how'd you think we got all our cows?

So that's why you stay here?

The Observers yearn for metal too and they pay best of all. I believe they fear the power of our magic.

Perhaps... but they control everything around here. After work we'll take you to see their temple.

Is it stronger than theirs?

Boatmen's
islands

The Stoneland

Long West River

Flint
mines

Great South River

At Sion in the Swiss Alps
prehistoric carved stones
called stelae
depict
Beaker People

The Archer
probably grew up
in this region

The Amesbury Archer might have made one journey or many.

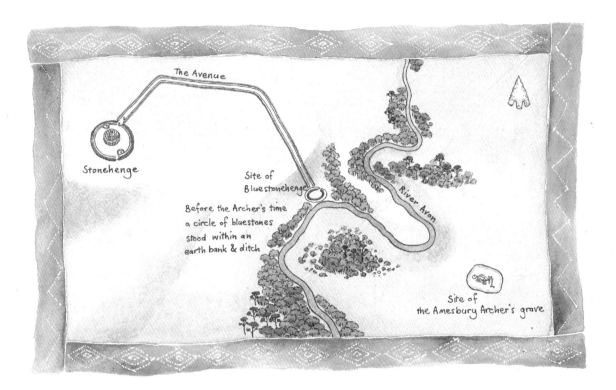

The map shows:

The Avenue

Stonehenge

Site of Bluestonehenge

Before the Archer's time a circle of bluestones stood within an earth bank & ditch

River Avon

Site of the Amesbury Archer's grave

The Archaeological Story ...

At Amesbury, near Stonehenge, in 2002 archaeologists unearthed the bones of a prehistoric man.

His mourners had placed precious objects in his grave including a pair of rare hair tress rings made from beaten gold. Together with three copper daggers, also buried with him, they are the oldest metal artefacts discovered in Britain.

The Finds

When Professor Andrew Fitzpatrick and his team examined the objects they found that many had come from mainland Europe, though some were from the British Isles. The five bell-shaped pots were Beakers, so called by archaeologists because they appear to have been drinking cups.

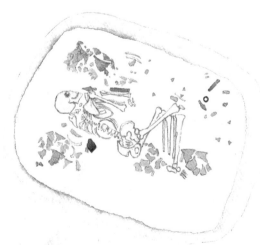

Grave of the Archer discovered at Amesbury, 4 km S.E. of Stonehenge. One of the richest burials in Europe of its time: 2300 B.C.

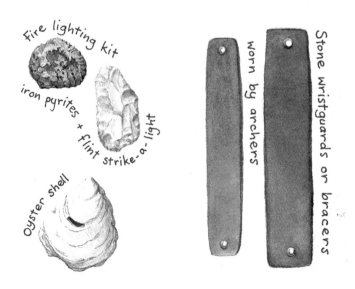

Fire lighting kit

iron pyrites + flint strike-a-light

Oyster shell

worn by archers

Stone wristguards or bracers

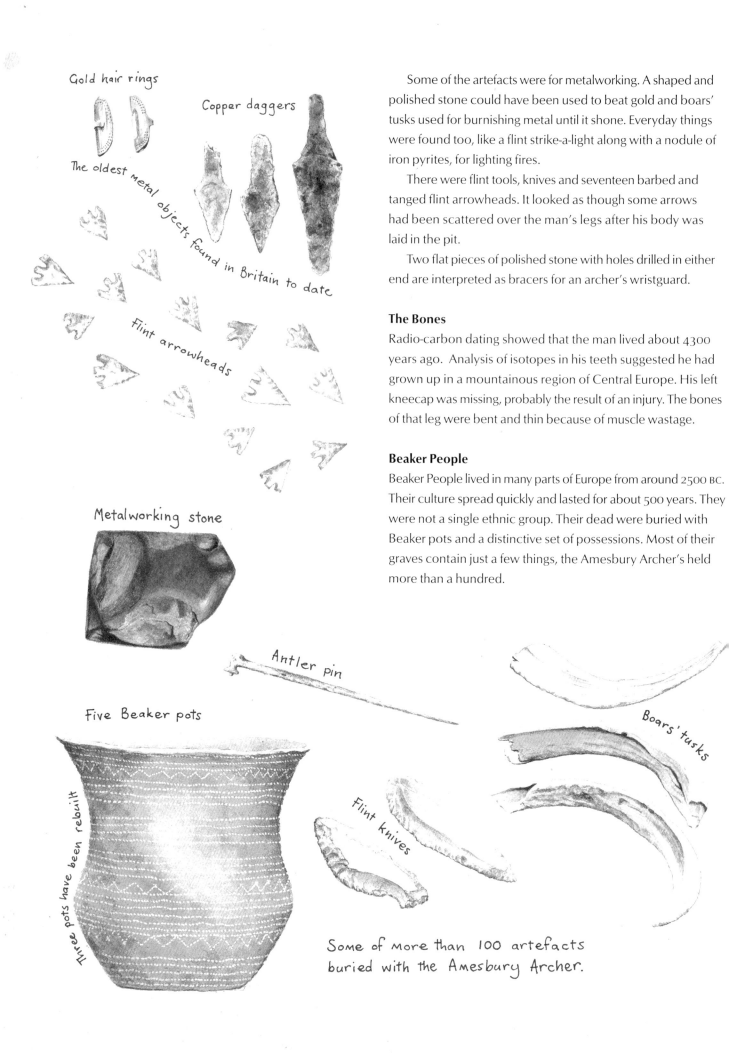

Gold hair rings

Copper daggers

The oldest metal objects found in Britain to date

Flint arrowheads

Metalworking stone

Some of the artefacts were for metalworking. A shaped and polished stone could have been used to beat gold and boars' tusks used for burnishing metal until it shone. Everyday things were found too, like a flint strike-a-light along with a nodule of iron pyrites, for lighting fires.

There were flint tools, knives and seventeen barbed and tanged flint arrowheads. It looked as though some arrows had been scattered over the man's legs after his body was laid in the pit.

Two flat pieces of polished stone with holes drilled in either end are interpreted as bracers for an archer's wristguard.

The Bones

Radio-carbon dating showed that the man lived about 4300 years ago. Analysis of isotopes in his teeth suggested he had grown up in a mountainous region of Central Europe. His left kneecap was missing, probably the result of an injury. The bones of that leg were bent and thin because of muscle wastage.

Beaker People

Beaker People lived in many parts of Europe from around 2500 BC. Their culture spread quickly and lasted for about 500 years. They were not a single ethnic group. Their dead were buried with Beaker pots and a distinctive set of possessions. Most of their graves contain just a few things, the Amesbury Archer's held more than a hundred.

Antler pin

Boars' tusks

Five Beaker pots

Three pots have been rebuilt

Flint knives

Some of more than 100 artefacts buried with the Amesbury Archer.